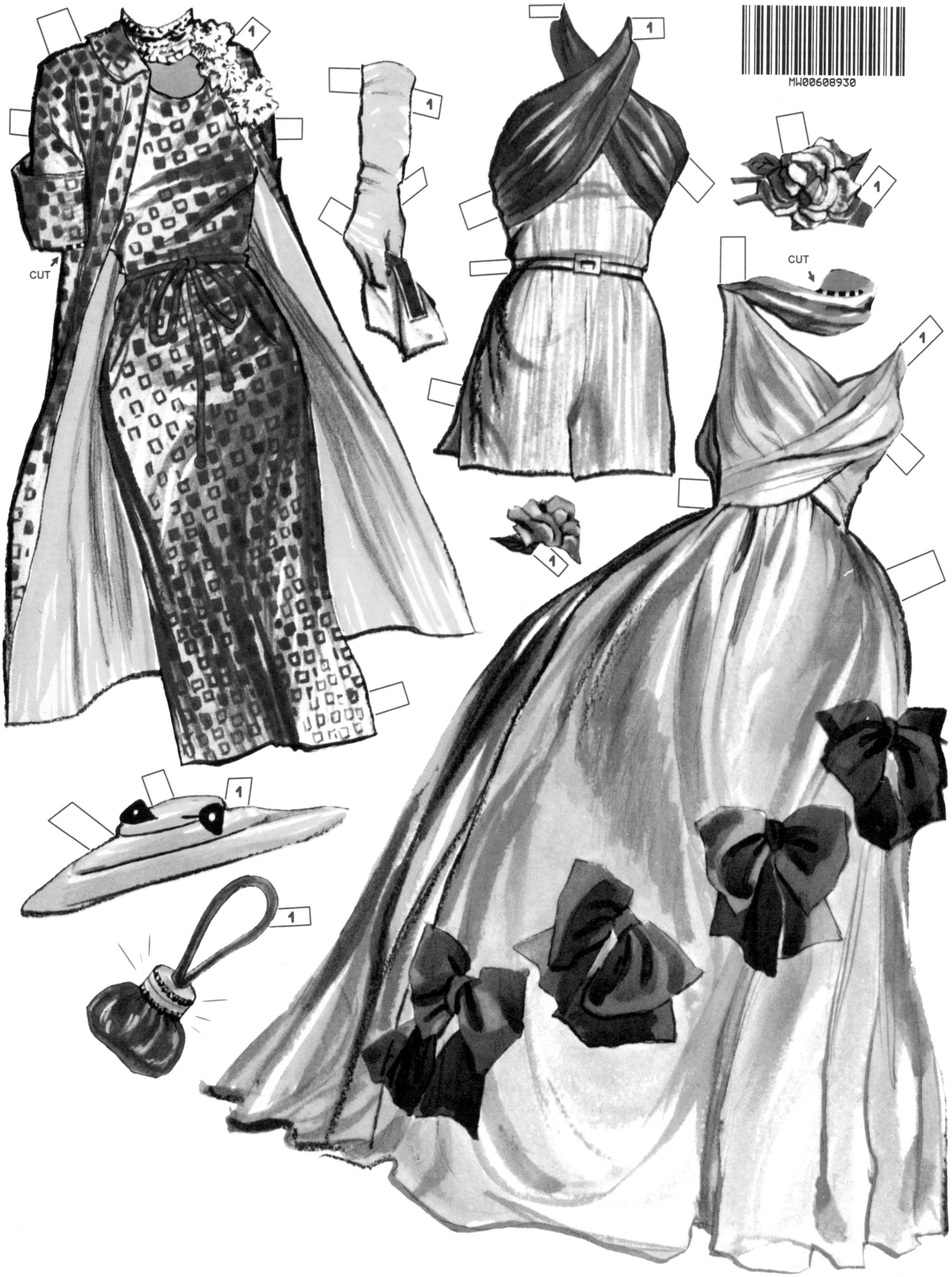


MW00608930

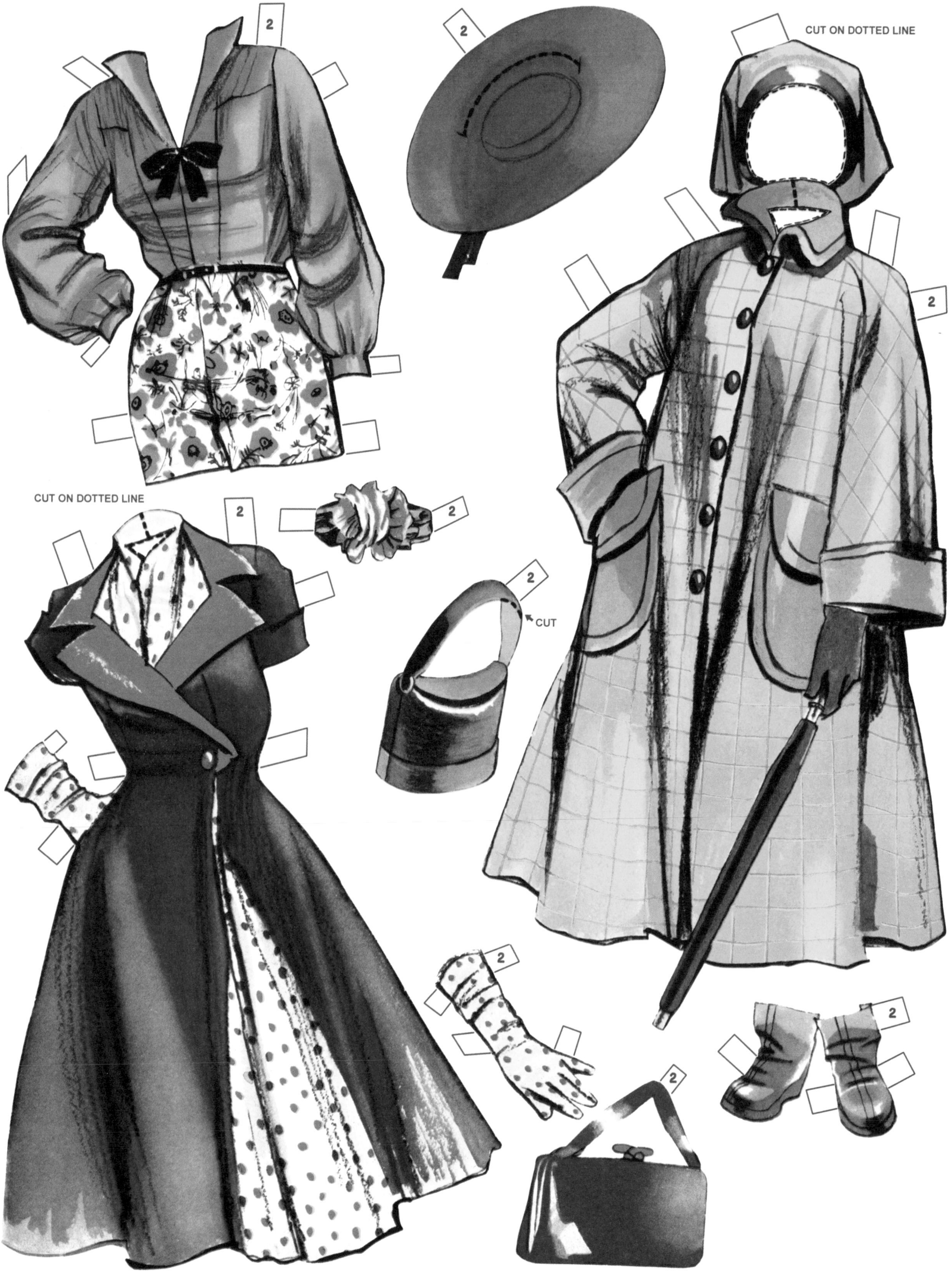
CUT ON DOTTED LINE
CUT ON DOTTED LINE
CUT
2

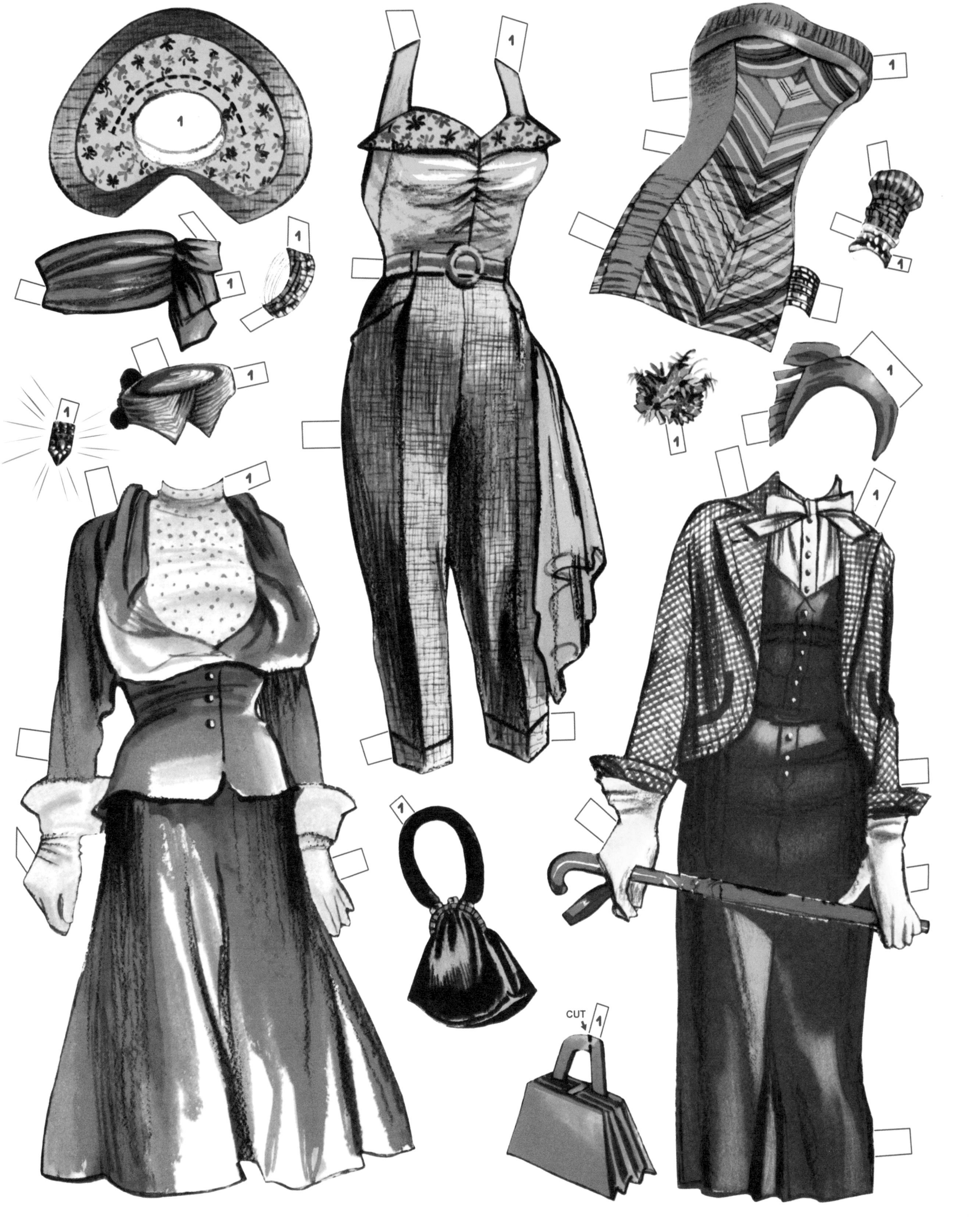
CUT
1

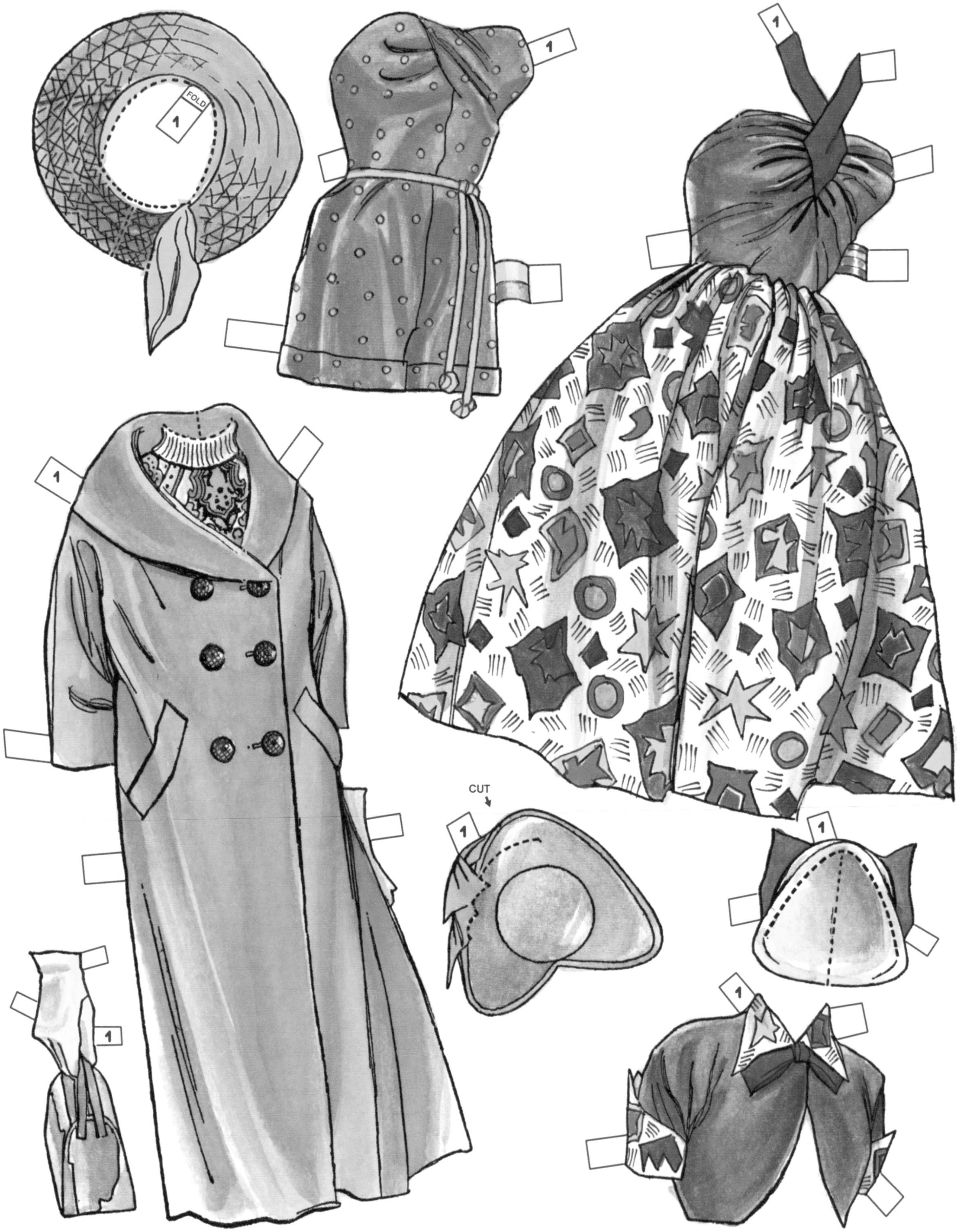
FOLD
1
1
1
1
CUT
1
1
1
1

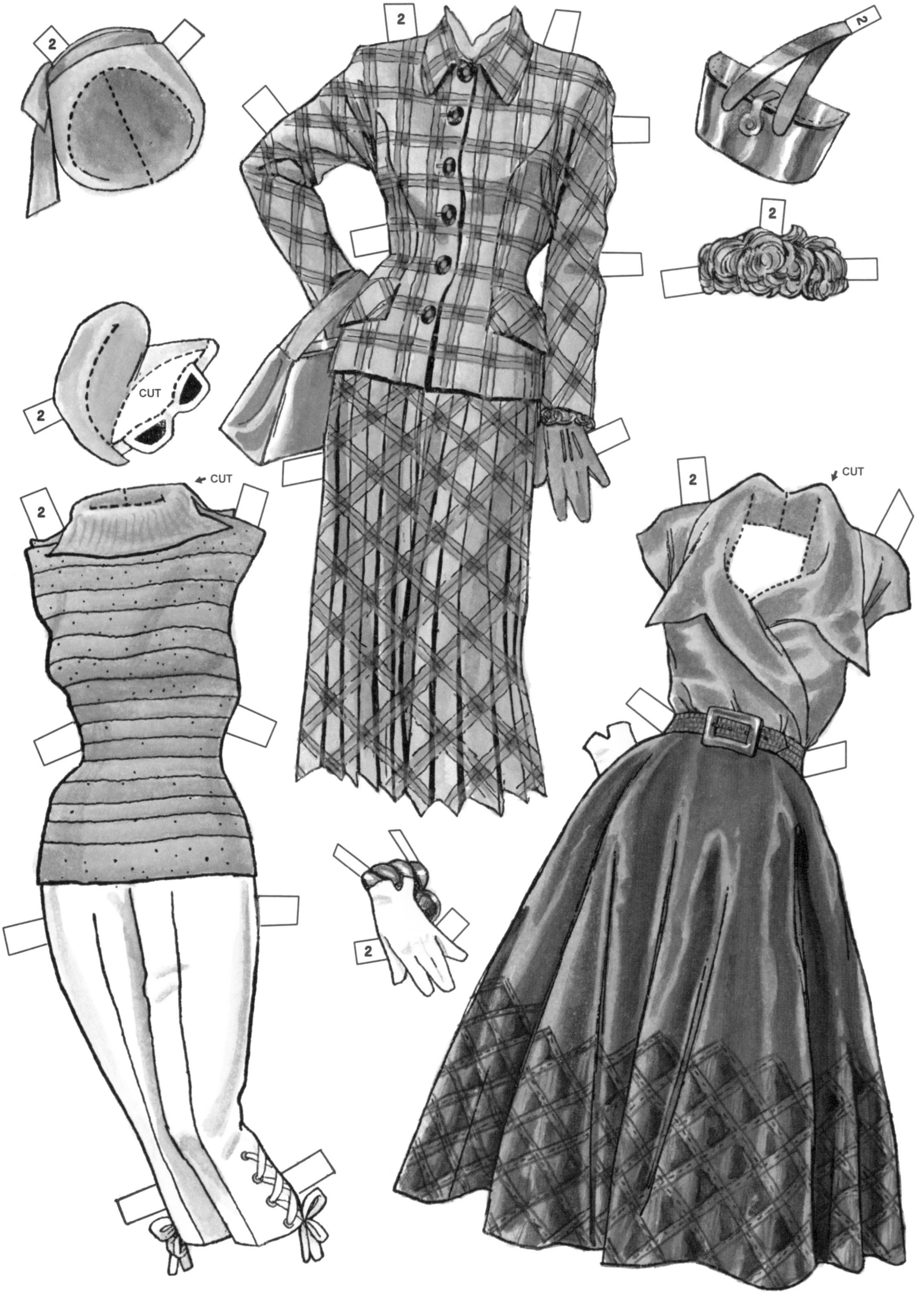
2
2
2
2
CUT
2
CUT
2
2
CUT
2

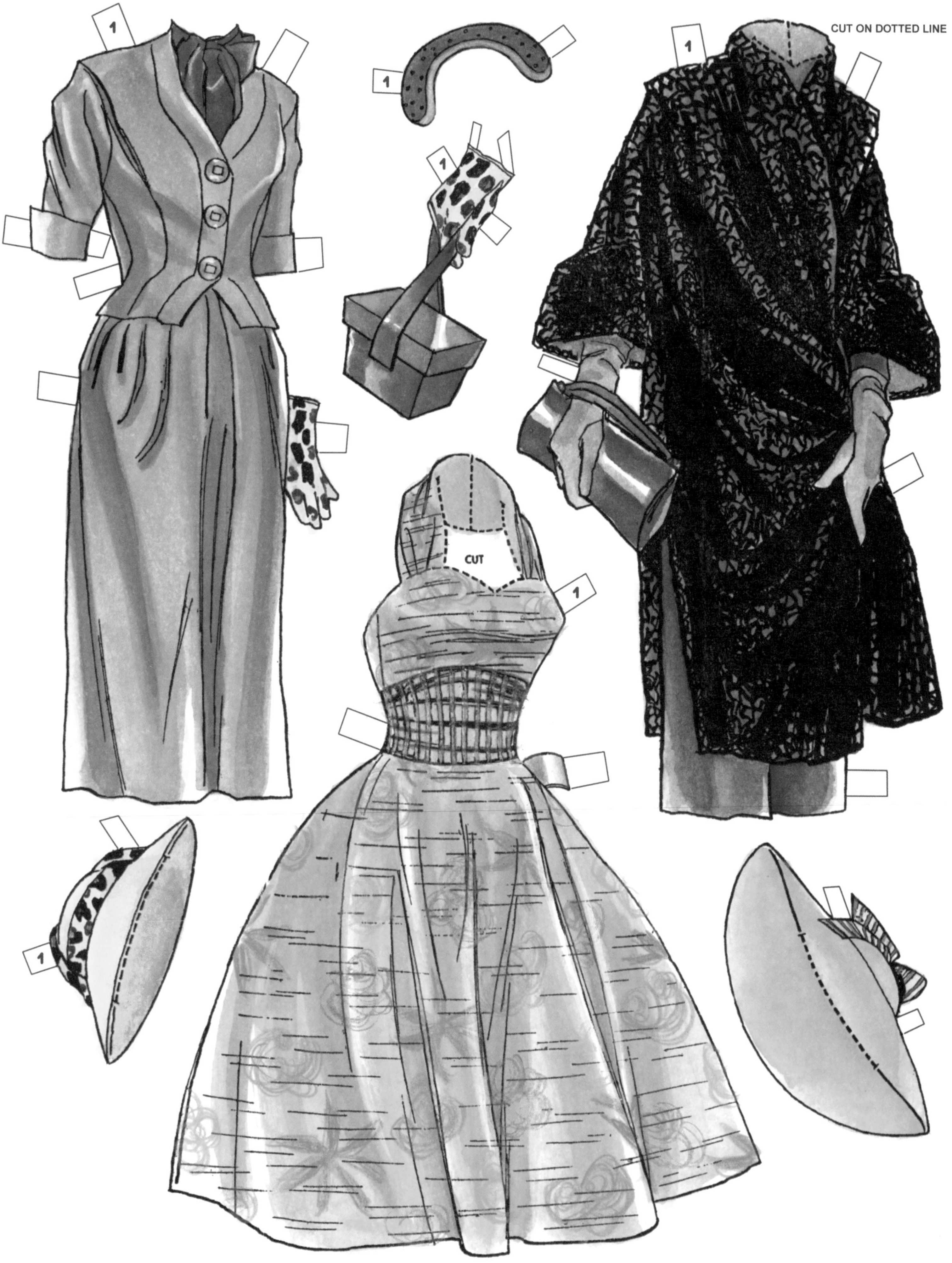

CUT ON DOTTED LINE
CUT
1
1
1
1
1
1

CUT ON DOTTED LINE

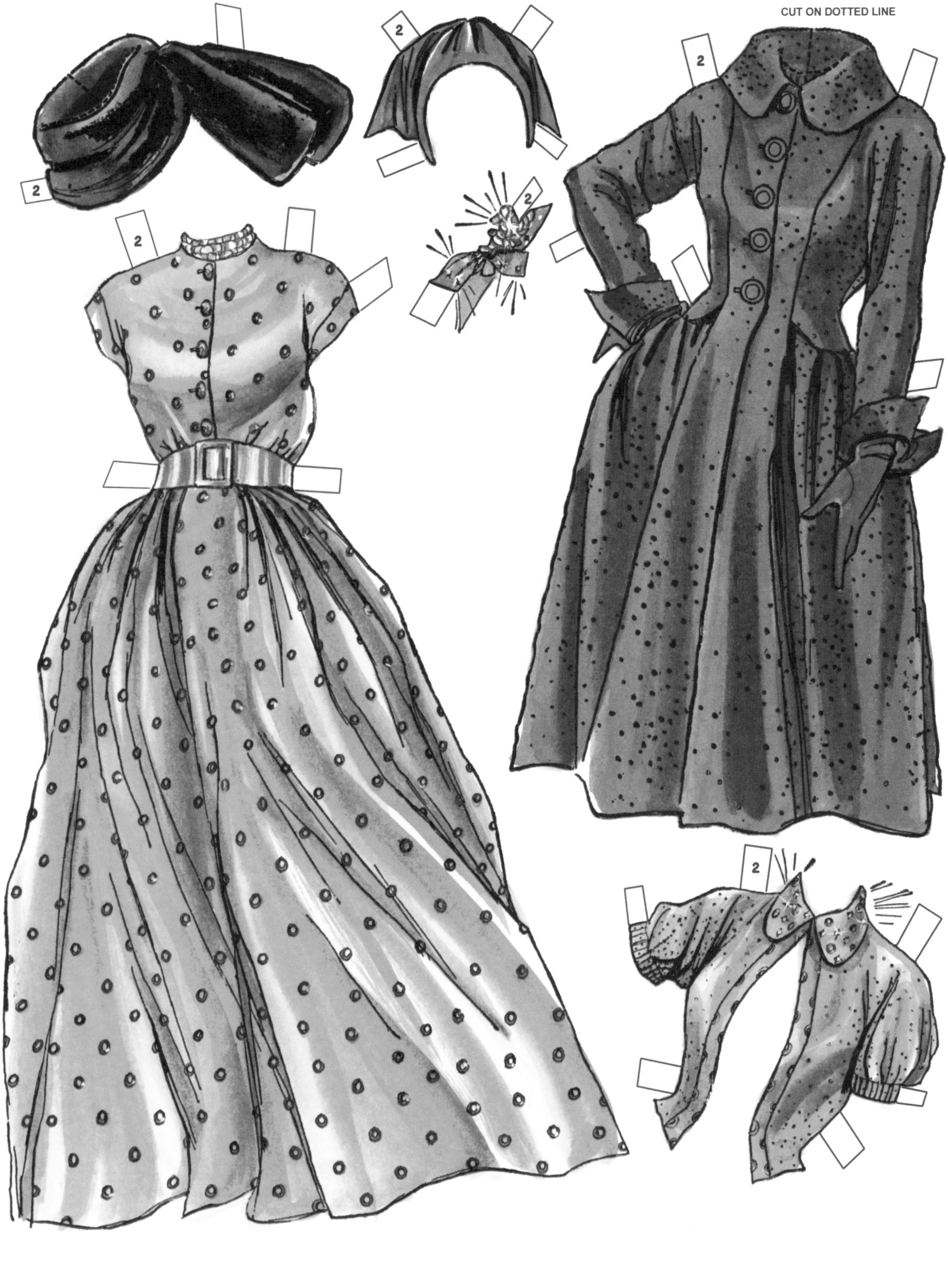

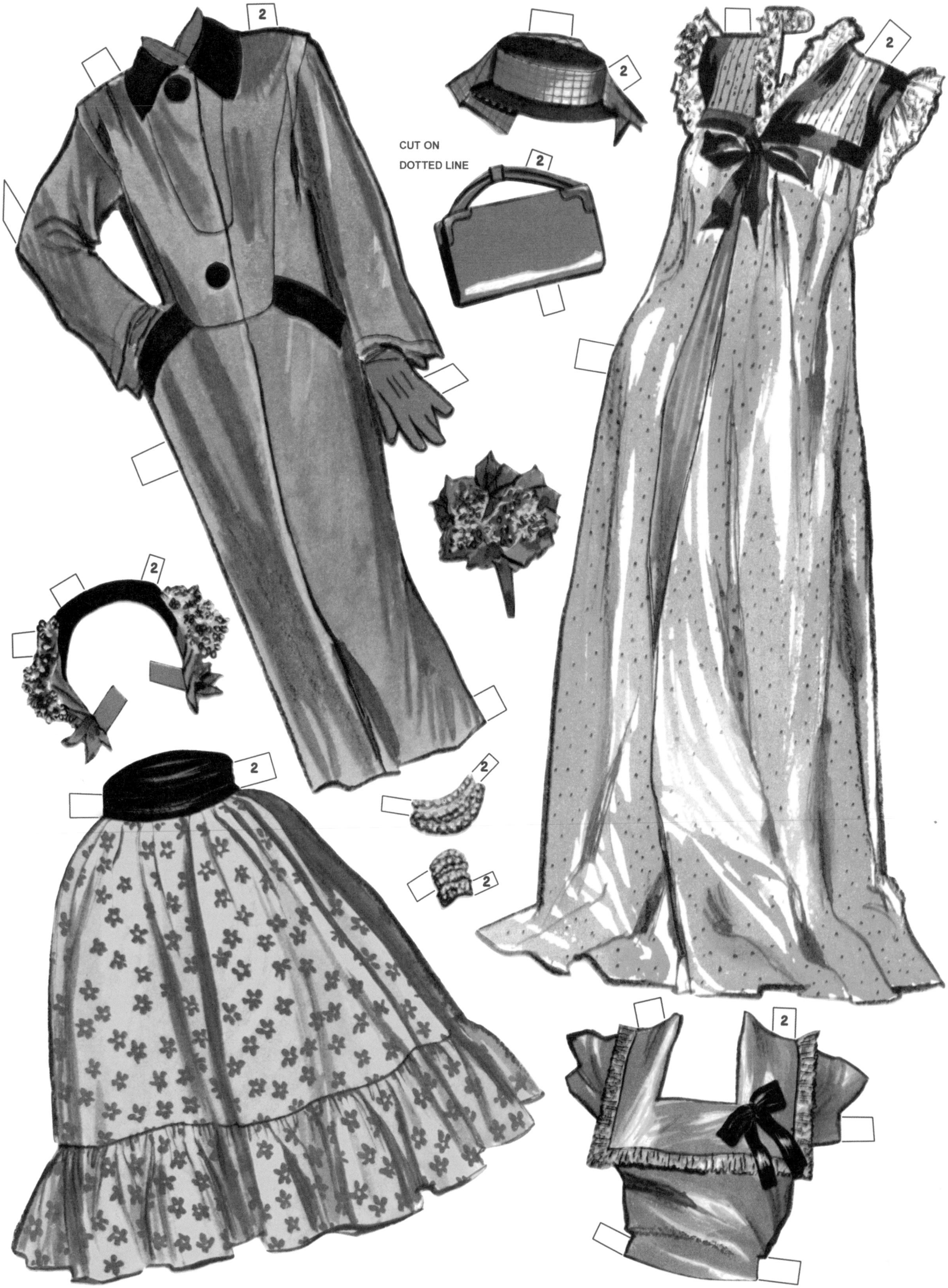
CUT ON
DOTTED LINE